Holes

Grades 4-6

Written by Nat Reed
Illustrated by Ric Ward

ISBN 1-55035-740-9
Copyright 2003
Revised March 2007
All Rights Reserved * Printed in Canada

Published in the United States by:
On The Mark Press
3909 Witmer Road PMB 175
Niagara Falls, New York 14305
www.onthemarkpress.com

Published in Canada by:
S&S Learning Materials
15 Dairy Avenue
Napanee, Ontario K7R 1M4
www.sslearning.com

Look For Other Junior - Novel Studies

HOLES

By Louis Sachar

Table of Contents

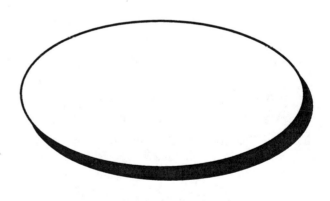

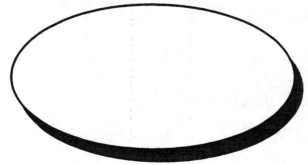

HOLES

By Louis Sachar

Expectations

The students will:

- develop their skills in reading, writing, listening and oral communication
- use good literature as a vehicle for developing skills required by curriculum expectations: reasoning and critical thinking, knowledge of language structure, vocabulary building, and use of conventions
- become meaningfully engaged in the drama of literature through a variety of types of questions and activities
- learn and review many skills in order to develop good reading habits
- provide clear answers to questions and well-constructed explanations
- organize and classify information to clarify thinking
- express and respond to a range of ideas and opinions concisely, clearly and appropriately
- relate events and feelings found in novels to their own lives and experiences
- appreciate the importance of friendship and loyalty in interpersonal relationships
- learn the importance of dealing with adversity and developing perseverance in the face of adversity

Teacher Suggestions

This book can be used in a variety of ways:

1. The student Booklet focuses on two chapters of the novel at a time. Each of these sections contains the following activities:

    Before you read the chapters (reasoning and critical thinking skills)
    Vocabulary building (dictionary and thesaurus skills)
    Questions on the two chapters (reading comprehension skills)
    Language activities (grammar, punctuation and word structure)

2. Students may read the novel at their own speed and then select, or be assigned, a variety of questions and activities.

3. **Bulletin Board and Interest Center Ideas:** themes might include desert life (both plant and animal); wilderness survival; racial prejudice; the justice system (as it pertains to youth); onions and peaches.

4. **Pre-Reading Activities:** *Holes* may also be used in conjunction with themes about self-esteem, friendship and loyalty in the face of adversity. Simulation activities dealing with wilderness survival may be introduced to students. What skills and supplies would be necessary for surviving a harsh desert environment?

5. **Independent Reading Approach:** Students who are able to work independently may attempt to complete the assignments in a self-directed manner. Initially these students should participate in the pre-reading activities with the rest of the class. Students should familiarize themselves with the reproducible student booklet. Completed worksheets should be submitted so that the teacher can note how quickly and accurately the students are working. Students may be brought together periodically to discuss issues in specific sections of the novel.

6. **Fine Arts Activities:** students may investigate the art and music of the native peoples (e.g. Apaches) of the desert areas of North America.

7. **Physical Activities:** Students may be taken on a nature walk with instructions to try to find animal life similar to that referred to in the novel.

8. Encourage students to keep a reading log in which they record their reading each day and their thoughts about the reading.

HOLES
By Louis Sachar

9. Students should keep all their work together in one place. A portfolio cover is provided for this reason.

10. Students should not be expected to complete all activities. Teachers should allow choice and in some cases match the activity to the student's ability.

11. Students should keep track (in their portfolio) of the activities they complete.

List of Skills

Vocabulary Development:
1. Identifying similes and metaphors
2. Locating descriptive words and phrases
3. Listing antonyms
4. Listing synonyms
5. Listing compound words
6. Using context clues; analogies; root words
7. Identifying parts of speech
8. Determining alphabetical order

Setting Activities:
1. Summarize the details of a setting
2. Create a time chart
3. List dangers and survival tips described in the novel
4. Map the route
5. Create a story map

Plot Activities:
1. Complete a *time line* of events
2. Analyze cause and effect
3. Sequence the main events from the novel
4. Identify conflict in the story
5. Determine the role played by conscience in the story

Character Activities:
1. Determine character traits
2. Illustrate and describe a character
3. Identify the use of personification
4. Compare two characters
5. Relating personal experiences and feelings to story
6. Understanding concepts such as *perseverance* and *self-respect*
7. Identify characteristics of a leader

Creative and Critical Thinking:
1. Research the yellow spotted lizard
2. Identify emotions and instincts as a help or hindrance
3. Write an editorial expressing an opinion
4. Write a letter to a local newspaper
5. Write a description of personal feelings
6. Decision-making exercise
7. Conduct an interview

Art Activities:
1. Illustrate a scene
2. Create a poster advertising Zero's disappearance
3. Design a brochure of Camp Green Lake
4. Investigate the art and music of the Native People of a desert region

Synopsis

Not much has gone right for Stanley Yelnats during his young life, so he isn't too surprised when he is mistakenly convicted of stealing a pair running shoes and sent to Camp Green Lake.

Camp Green Lake is an unusual detention center situated on the edge of a sunburned wasteland, where each day Stanley and the other boys are forced to dig holes exactly five feet wide, and five feet deep. Here Stanley earns the nickname, *Caveman*, learns valuable lessons about endurance and hard work, and meets a fascinating cast of fellow residents: Zero, X-Ray, Magnet, and Armpit.

HOLES

By Louis Sachar

Stanley soon realizes they are not digging holes simply to build character but the Warden is in fact looking for a lost treasure – one buried years before by Kissing Kate Barlow, a notorious western outlaw. Kissing Kate's adventures form a fascinating parallel story – one with links to Stanley's "no-good-dirty-rotten-pig-stealing-great-great-grandfather".

Stanley, meanwhile, uncovers the spot where Kissing Kate buried her stolen treasure, but keeps the location a secret. Unable to tolerate the abuse at Camp Green Lake any longer, Stanley and Zero escape into the desert, heading for a spot known as God's Finger. After a long, arduous journey, the boys manage to survive on an onion patch planted many years before. Recovering their strength Stanley and Zero decide to return to the camp at night to dig up the treasure.

Caught in the act of unearthing the buried treasure by the evil warden, Stanley and Zero are saved from further punishment by the timely arrival of Stanley's parents who arrive with orders for Stanley's release.

Holes is action-packed with a cast of endearing characters. The novel also deals in a very entertaining manner with important themes such as self-acceptance and racial prejudices.

Author Biography

Louis Sachar

Louis Sachar was born March 20, 1954 in East Meadow, New York, but moved to California with his family when he was nine-years-old. He now lives in Austin, Texas. As a boy, Louis enjoyed playing Little League and reading, especially stories by authors such as E.B. White.

Louis attended college in Ohio and the University of California, majoring in economics. He spent time selling Fuller Brush door to-door and worked at a sweater warehouse in Connecticut.

It was his experience working as a teacher's aide that led him to write his first book, *Sideways Stories from Wayside School*, which was accepted for publication during his first week of law school. After several years of practicing law he gave up the profession in 1989 to write full time. "Writing was always my first love," he says.

Louis met his wife, Carla, when visiting a school in Texas where she was a counsellor. They have a daughter, Sherre.

Sachar says, "I just try to write books that are fun to read. I figure if I like them, they will too." He also likes his books to have a moral dimension, where his readers are challenged to think about right and wrong.

It takes Louis about a year and a half to write a book. In his spare time he enjoys playing bridge and tennis.

Holes has received the National Book Award for Young People's Literature, and the Newbery Medal, the highest honor accorded to children's literature in the United States.

Some of the novels written by Louis Sachar:
Sideways Stories from Wayside School, ©1978
Someday, Angeline, ©1983
Sixth Grade Secrets, ©1987
There's a Boy in the Girls' Bathroom, ©1987
Dogs Don't Tell Jokes, ©1991
Marvin Redpost: Why Pick on Me?, ©1993
The Boy Who Lost His Face, ©1997

HOLES

By Louis Sachar

Student Checklist

Student Name: _____

Assignment	Grade / Level	Comments

HOLES

By Louis Sachar

Name: _____

HOLES
By Louis Sachar

Chapters 1 and 2

Before you read the chapters:

Describe a time when you were extremely hot.

_____

_____

_____

_____

Rattlesnakes and scorpions are very dangerous. What animal, reptile or insect, frightens you the most?

_____

Why do you think this creature is so frightening?

_____

_____

_____

Vocabulary:

Choose a word from the list that means the same or nearly the same as the underlined word.

hammock	hover	shriveled	forbidden	warden

1. Kevin knew that entering his neighbor's property was **against the law**.

   _____

2. The space ship seemed to **float** above the ground. _____

3. Clarice took a nap in the **hanging bed**. _____

4. The prison's **top official** ran the jail with an iron fist. _____

5. When the piece of leather was removed from the water it was shrunk and **wrinkled**.

   _____

 # HOLES

By Louis Sachar

Questions:

1. Camp Green Lake was an unusual place. Describe the climate of the area, the land around the camp, and examples of the animal life that lived there.

2. What would probably happen to a camper if bitten by the following:
   a) a rattlesnake: _____
   b) a scorpion: _____
   c) a yellow-spotted lizard: _____

3. What happened to the lake at Camp Green Lake?
   _____

4. What was a good rule to follow in dealing with rattlesnakes?
   _____

5. What two choices did the judge give to Stanley?
   _____   _____

6. What do you think Stanley might have been thinking when offered this choice?
   _____
   _____

7. Why hadn't Stanley been to camp before?
   _____
   _____

Language Activities:

Find **five** verbs from Chapters One and Two. Create your own adverb to go with each verb.

Example: Francine **played** left wing on the girls' hockey team – played **skillfully** (or **reluctantly**).

Skillfully and **reluctantly** are adverbs that could go with the verb 'played'.

_____
_____
_____
_____

HOLES
By Louis Sachar

Chapters 3 and 4

Before you read the chapters:

Think of a time when you had to travel to a destination which was new to you. Describe your feelings.

_____

_____

Describe a time when you were blamed for something you didn't do. How did you feel?

_____

_____

Vocabulary:

Draw a straight line to connect the vocabulary word to its definition. Remember to use a straight edge (like a ruler)?

1.	counselor	huge
2.	ratio	proportion
3.	obstacle	barrier
4.	convicted	abandoned
5.	Gypsy	canvas
6.	descendants	advisor
7.	vast	heirs
8.	desolate	to begin with
9.	burlap	vagabond
10.	originally	security
11.	protection	condemned

Questions:

1. What does "He was on a long bus ride to nowhere" mean?

_____

_____

2. Describe how Stanley's math teacher had embarrassed him.

_____

_____

 # HOLES

By Louis Sachar

3. What was Stanley's father trying to invent?

_____

_____

4. Why didn't Kate Barlow kiss Stanley's great grandfather?

_____

_____

5. Why do you think the author ended Chapter Three with the sentence, "And hardly anything was green."?

_____

_____

6. Describe Camp Green Lake.

_____

_____

7. Describe Stanley's new set of clothes.

_____

_____

8. What were the campers to do if they found anything interesting while digging their holes?

_____

_____

9. Why weren't there any guard towers or electric fences around the camp?

_____

_____

Language Activities:

Choose 10 words from Chapter 3 and 4 with two or more syllables. Then indicate the syllables by drawing a line after each syllable. **Example:** Stan/ley

_____   _____   _____   _____

_____   _____   _____   _____

_____   _____

Chapters 5 and 6

Before you read the chapters:

Nicknames can be fun or sometimes mean. Have you ever had a nickname? If so what was it? If not, why do you think you've never had one?

_____

_____

List the nicknames of three people with whom you are familiar.

_____   _____   _____

Meeting new people can be very stressful. Describe an experience when you met a group of people for the first time.

_____

_____

Not being believed can be very frustrating. Describe what it must feel like for a person not to be believed when he or she is telling the truth.

_____

_____

Vocabulary:

In each of the following sets of words, underline the one word which does not belong. Then write a sentence explaining why it does not fit.

1. sanitary	clean	shadow	antiseptic
2. early	despicable	contemptible	hateful
3. coincidence	leaflet	change	fluke
4. scarcity	lack	broccoli	absence
5. destiny	fate	providence	contorted

HOLES

By Louis Sachar

6. coax   spigot   tap   faucet

_____

7. compound   gather   mixture   blend

_____

Questions:

1. Who was Stanley's counselor? Describe his appearance.

_____

_____

2. Match each character with his nickname:

   a) Alan   Zero

   b) X-Ray   Squid

   c) Barf Bag   Mom

   d) Jose   Magnet

   e) Theodore   Zigzag

   f) Ricky   Armpit

   g) Mr. Pendanski   Rex

   h) Zero   Lewis

3. According to Mr. Pendanski, why did they call Zero by that nickname?

_____

_____

4. Why do you think Armpit liked his nickname?

_____

_____

5. What was Clyde Livingston's nickname?

_____

_____

6. What were two special feats that Clyde Livingston accomplished in his baseball career?

_____

_____

7. Why did Stanley's story about how he came to have the running shoes seem so unbelievable to the judge?

_____

_____

8. Why did Stanley's mother feel that he didn't need a lawyer? Do you think this is a good idea?

_____

_____

9. Why do you think Stanley blamed everything on his no-good-dirty-rotten-pig-stealing-great-great-grandfather?

_____

_____

Language Activities:

Mr. Pendanski's name was easy to remember because of three easy words which sound like his name:

_____   _____   _____

Can you think of a similar name made up of three easy words?

_____   _____   _____

HOLES

By Louis Sachar

Chapters 7 and 8

Before you read the chapters:

Both Stanley and his great-great-grandfather are offered advice in Chapter 7. Describe why it is important for someone to follow good advice.

_____

_____

How might it be possible to distinguish good from bad advice?

_____

_____

Research the yellow spotted lizard. Find out three facts about this creature.

_____

_____

Vocabulary:

Synonyms are words with similar meanings. Use the context of the sentences below to help you choose the best synonym for the underlined word in each sentence. If you cannot determine the meaning from the context, consult a dictionary.

1. He glanced helplessly at his shovel. It wasn't **defective**. He was defective.
   a) faulty   **b)** able   **c)** arrogant   **d)** charming

2. Madame Zeroni hated to see Elya so **forlorn**.
   a) glorious   **b)** happy   **c)** discouraged   **d)** poor

3. Stanley was dumping his dirt within the **perimeter** of his hole.
   a) bottom   **b)** inside   **c)** middle   **d)** border

4. He **grimaced** as he sliced off a chunk of dirt.
   a) smiled   **b)** scowled   **c)** hesitated   **d)** laughed

5. "that's **preposterous**," exclaimed Igor.
   a) crazy   **b)** wonderful   **c)** wet   **d)** selfish

6. When the dirt was in the ground it was **compacted**.
   a) filthy   **b)** packed   **c)** wet   **d)** loose

7. He **deftly** removed the seeds from the shells.
   a) slowly   **b)** ably   **c)** slyly   **d)** timidly

HOLES

By Louis Sachar

Questions:

1. For what reason were the boys told they were digging the holes?

   _____

   _____

2. Why did the digging get easier as the hole got deeper?

   _____

   _____

3. What did Stanley's grandfather offer for the hand of Myra?

   _____

   _____

4. Describe Madame Zeroni's opinion of Myra as well as the strategy she suggested.

   _____

   _____

5. What was the curse that Elya would have to endure if he failed to fulfill his end of the bargain?

   _____

   _____

6. What did Stanley use to protect his blistered hands?

   _____

   _____

7. Why did Zigzag think Zero was "one weird dude"?

   _____

   _____

8. Why do you think Elya looked for Madame Zeroni's son in America?

   _____

   _____

9. What was the last thing that Stanley did before starting back for the camp after digging the hole?

   _____

   _____

10. Chapter 8 begins with a sentence about curses, but, instead of curses, what is the main topic of the chapter?

   _____

   _____

11. Why do you think the author begins the chapter with a sentence about curses?

   _____

   _____

Language Activities:

Write the plural of the following nouns from Chapters 7 and 8:

person: _____

lullaby: _____

chunk: _____

cactus: _____

canteen: _____

woman: _____

thumb: _____

HOLES
By Louis Sachar

Chapters 9 and 10

Before you read the chapters:

Stanley learns two very important lessons in these two chapters: standing up for himself, and enduring a very trying experience.

Describe an experience from your own life where you either stood up for yourself when being bullied, or you endured a very difficult time.

_____

_____

_____

Vocabulary:

Use a dictionary to find the meanings of the following words:

sprawled: _____

vinyl: _____

intensity: _____

commercial: _____

miracle: _____

awesome: _____

fossilized: _____

blistered: _____

HOLES

By Louis Sachar

Questions:

1. Describe the "Wreck Room". Why was this an appropriate name?

2. What reasons did X-Ray offer for considering the second hole to be the hardest?

3. Why do you think Stanley wrote such a glowing letter to his mother?

4. What was Stanley's new nickname? Why do you think the other boys chose this name for him?

5. Describe how Stanley felt when he got up the morning after his first full day of digging.

6. What was strange about Stanley finding the shape of a fossilized fish in the rock?

7. Why did finding the fossil give Stanley hope?

Language Activities:

When Stanley writes a letter home in Chapter 9, he hides the truth about Camp Green Lake from his mother.

Pretend that after a particularly harsh day Stanley decides to write a letter to the local newspaper describing the harsh treatment he has received at Camp Green Lake, mentioning specifically the behavior of the warden or guards.

Remember this should follow the format of the personal letter you have practiced.

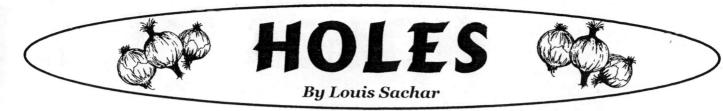

HOLES
By Louis Sachar

Chapters 11 and 12

Before you read the chapters:

Even though he was the smallest of the group, X-Ray was the leader of the boys. What do you think are three important characteristics in being a recognized leader?

_____

_____

_____

Mr. Pendanski encourages the boys to think about what they will do with their lives. Describe your own plans for your life.

_____

_____

_____

Vocabulary:

Choose a word from the list to complete each definition.

senseless	smug	obvious	veterinarian	accomplish
responsible	expand	appropriate	expression	society

1. A proud person is said to be _____.

2. A police officer is usually a person who is _____.

3. When something is as plain as the nose on your face, it is _____.

4. An animal doctor is a _____.

5. Something that is absurd is said to be _____.

6. To achieve is to _____.

7. Something which grows in size is said to _____.

8. A group of people or a civilization is a _____.

9. A thing which is agreeable or acceptable is _____.

10. A statement or adage is an _____.

HOLES

By Louis Sachar

Questions:

1. What hindered X-Ray from finding anything of value while digging?
   _____
   _____

2. Why did Stanley find it surprising that X-Ray was the leader of the group?
   _____
   _____

3. How do you think X-Ray got to be leader?
   _____
   _____

4. Why was Stanley glad that the boys called him Caveman?
   _____
   _____

5. Describe Stanley's fantasy about the school bully, Derrick Duane.
   _____
   _____

6. "After all, you only have one life, so you should try to make the most of it." Sound advice from Mr. Pendanski. Suggest two ways of making the most of one's life.
   _____
   _____

7. When questioned by Mr. Pendanski, on whom did Stanley blame his problems?
   _____
   _____

8. Why do you think Zero said that he liked to dig holes?
   _____
   _____

9. "Even you, Zero, you're not completely worthless." (Mr. Pendanski) What do you think Mr. Pendanski is really saying about Zero?
   _____
   _____

Language Activities:

X-Ray mentions that his nickname is **pig latin** for Rex, his real name. Investigate the rules of pig latin, and give **three** examples.

HOLES
By Louis Sachar

Chapters 13 and 14

Before you read the chapters:

These chapters are about a buried treasure. What might be three examples of a not-so-obvious, valuable, buried treasure?

_____ _____ _____

If you were going to bury four personal valuables, what might they be?

_____ _____ _____ _____

Vocabulary:

Replace the words that are underlined in the sentences below with a word from the word list in the box. Remember to consider the context of the word in the sentence, as some words have several meanings.

chose	occasionally	glisten	sifted	design
engraved	produce	turquoise	nervous	authority

1. The warden **decided** to give the campers a day off. _____

2. He will be going shopping **once in a while**. _____

3. The trophy began to **gleam** in the sunlight. _____

4. She was wearing an **aquamarine-colored** sweater. _____

5. The general had **command** over her troops. _____

6. I hope to **create** a fine painting this summer. _____

7. Stanley **filtered** the sand through his fingers. _____

8. There was an outstanding **pattern** on the vase. _____

9. A person's initials were **etched** on the inside of the bracelet. _____

10. He was very **edgy** on Halloween night. _____

 # HOLES

By Louis Sachar

Questions:

1. Why did the boys think the cloud was "teasing them"?

   _____

   _____

2. Describe what Stanley found while digging.

   _____

   _____

3. What plan did Stanley suggest to X-Ray?

   _____

   _____

4. How did X-Ray reward Stanley?

   _____

   _____

5. Describe your impression of the warden. Support your answer.

   _____

   _____

6. Why did Mr. Pendanski object to filling the canteens?

   _____

   _____

Language Activities:

An **adjective** is a word which describes a noun. It gives the reader a clear picture of what the author sees.

> **Example:** "Now Green Lake was just a dry, flat wasteland."

Write a paragraph describing the setting of *Holes*. Make sure to use adjectives to illustrate your ideas.

_____

_____

_____

_____

_____

_____

 # HOLES
By Louis Sachar

Chapters 15 and 16

Before you read the chapters:

The Warden is determined to find missing treasure. Predict what you think will happen as a result of these efforts.

_____

_____

_____

Vocabulary:

Write a sentence using the following words. Make sure that the meaning of the word is clear in your sentence.

excavated: _____

_____

squid: _____

_____

paranoid: _____

_____

presumably: _____

_____

evict: _____

_____

previously: _____

_____

character: _____

_____

compound: _____

_____

 # HOLES

By Louis Sachar

Questions:

1. Why did the Warden have the boys dig X-Ray's hole twice?

   _____

   _____

2. Why did Stanley know they wouldn't find anything in X-Ray's pile of dirt?

   _____

   _____

3. How was the Warden able to "keep an eye" on the boys at all times?

   _____

   _____

4. Why do you suppose Stanley "dug the hole into his memory"?

   _____

   _____

5. What was ironic about the Warden's remark to X-Ray, "We need your sharp eyes"?

   _____

   _____

6. Why was Stanley's mother proud of him?

   _____

   _____

7. Why do you think Zero had never heard of Sesame Street?

   _____

   _____

Language Activities:

A **compound** word is a word that is made of two words put together. **Examples:** outline, groundhog. Find and list **10** compound words from Chapters 15 and 16. Draw a line between the words that are being combined.

_____   _____   _____

_____   _____   _____

_____   _____   _____

_____

HOLES

By Louis Sachar

Chapters 17 and 18

Before you read the chapters:

Describe what you think it must feel like to be knocked unconscious. You can base your answer on experience or imagination.

_____

_____

Vocabulary:

The words in the following list can be found in the word search. Circle each one in the puzzle and put a check mark beside the word in the list.

supposedly	realize	underneath	wheelbarrows
gash	wound	throbbing	section
imagined	digger	stationery	shovel
relief	callused	crate	laugh
moisture	muscles	energy	

```
c a l l u s e d a v d n u o w
l r w e t m u s c l e s g g t
q a a r t h n s h o v e l a h
a i u t g u d w q v w n a s r
e o b g e n e r g y o o r h o
q p a q h m r e r e l i e f b
s t a t i o n e r y l t a e b
i m a g i n e d e n e c l r i
e x c v b n a f r b n e i t n
r r m o i s t u r e m s z y g
y x c v b m h m d i g g e r p
u s u p p o s e d l y k l o p
i r b s w o r r a b l e e h w
```

 # HOLES

By Louis Sachar

Questions:

1. Describe how Stanley was injured.

2. How long did it take the boys to dig until all three holes met and formed one hole?

3. Why do you think Squid's answer to the warden was the wrong thing to say?

4. Why did Stanley stay in his tent to write a letter to his mother?

5. Describe Stanley's opinion of Zero. Why do you think he felt that way?

6. What didn't Zero know how to do?

7. Besides Stanley's muscles and hands, what other part of him had toughened up?

Language Activities:

Rewrite the following sentences putting in the correct capitalization and punctuation.

1. mr penadaski was a guard at camp green lake

2. stanleys friends included armpit zero and magnet

3. clyde Livingston played for the chicago cubs

4. my favorite book is called lost in space

HOLES
By Louis Sachar

Chapters 19 and 20

Before you read the chapters:

Imagine three disadvantages of not being able to read and write.

_____

_____

Why do you think an innocent person would take the blame for something he or she didn't do?

_____

_____

Vocabulary:

Antonyms are words with opposite meanings. Draw a line from each word in column A to its antonym in column B. Then, use the words in column A to fill in the blanks in the sentences below.

Column A	Column B
1. agony	honored
2. ingredient	healthful
3. toxic	advance
4. condemned	invigoration
5. recede	product

1. The guilty man was _____ to 20 years in prison.

2. The tide began to _____ with the rising sun.

3. Stanley found the heat of the sun to be sheer _____.

4. The drinking water proved to be _____.

5. An important _____ of success is perseverance.

 # HOLES

By Louis Sachar

Questions:

1. Describe what Stanley meant when he said there were no racial problems among the boys.

   _____

   _____

2. Why do you think Squid was crying? On what did he blame his crying the next morning?

   _____

   _____

3. Describe how Stanley got into trouble over a bag of sunflower seeds.

   _____

   _____

4. Why do you think Stanley took the blame for stealing the bag? Who really did steal the sunflowers? Describe how he must have felt when Stanley confessed.

   _____

   _____

   _____

5. Why didn't Mr. Sir believe Stanley had stolen the sunflowers?

   _____

   _____

6. What was there about the Warden's dark-red nail polish that was special?

   _____

   _____

7. What did the Warden do to Mr. Sir? Why do you think she did this?

   _____

   _____

Language Activities:

There are many examples of **similes** in this novel (a comparison using the words **like** or **as**). In Chapter 19, Magnet says, "My fingers are like little magnets".

Create three similes of your own. Make them as creative and imaginative as possible.

_____

_____

_____

HOLES
By Louis Sachar

Chapters 21 and 22

Before you read the chapters:

Describe an experience when you learned to do something valuable or interesting.

_____

_____

How did you feel about this experience?

_____

_____

Vocabulary:

Draw a straight line to connect the vocabulary word to its definition. Remember to use a strait edge (like a ruler)!

1.	desolate	haven
2.	insane	comfort
3.	refuge	quote
4.	expand	wound
5.	relief	invigorate
6.	reconsider	abandoned
7.	recite	grow
8.	astonishment	small letters
9.	lowercase	surprise
10.	coiled	demented
11.	refresh	modify

Questions:

1. Why do you suppose Stanley wanted to finish digging his hole before Mr. Sir recovered?

_____

_____

HOLES

By Louis Sachar

2. How long had Stanley's great grandfather survived in the desert after being left by Kissin' Kate? Where had he found refuge?

   _____

   _____

3. Why did Stanley say that a rattlesnake would be a lot more dangerous if it didn't have a rattle?

   _____

   _____

4. Who dug Stanley's hole? How do you know? Why do you think he did this?

   _____

   _____

5. How do you know Zero was good at math?

   _____

   _____

6. What did Zero agree to do in exchange for Stanley teaching him to read? How did Stanley justify Zero's part of the deal?

   _____

   _____

7. Where had Stanley seen the gold tube before? What did he think it might be? Who did he think it might have belonged to?

   _____

   _____

Language Activities:

Try to reassemble the word parts listed below into 10 compound words.

stick	rattle	sun	every	grand	case	bath	one	waste	body
out	lip	land	flower	lower	snake	room	father	every	side

1. _____   6. _____

2. _____   7. _____

3. _____   8. _____

4. _____   9. _____

5. _____   10. _____

 # HOLES

By Louis Sachar

Chapters 23 and 24

Before you read the chapters:

Do you think it is important to stand up for oneself? Explain your answer.

_____

_____

Describe a situation in which either you (or someone you know) stood up for yourself.

_____

_____

Vocabulary:

Think of **synonyms** for the following words. Use a thesaurus if necessary.

grotesque: _____

_____

fabulous: _____

_____

delicious: _____

_____

obviously: _____

_____

reflected: _____

_____

incurable: _____

_____

disrespectful: _____

_____

ladled: _____

_____

absorbed: _____

_____

 # HOLES

By Louis Sachar

Questions:

1. What spices did Miss Katherine include in her spiced peaches?

    _____

    _____

2. What were Miss Katherine's peaches called?

    _____

    _____

3. What did Miss Katherine do for a living?

    _____

    _____

4. What affliction did Trout Walker have?

    _____

    _____

5. What kind of a guy was Trout? How do you know this?

    _____

    _____

6. Describe Mr. Sir's reaction when a boy asked what happened to his face.

    _____

    _____

7. What does it mean to "pace oneself"?

    _____

    _____

8. What mean thing did Mr. Sir do to Stanley?

    _____

    _____

Language Activities:

Miss Katherine was very proud of her spiced peaches. Investigate four things which can be made from peaches.

    _____   _____

    _____   _____

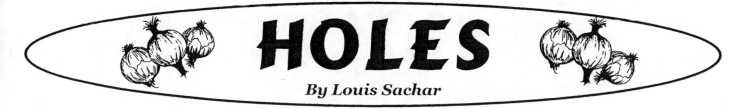

HOLES

By Louis Sachar

Chapters 25 and 26

Before you read the chapters:

Define **prejudice**: _____

_____

Give examples of victims of prejudice:_____

Why do you think some people are prejudiced?

_____

_____

Vocabulary:

Choose a word from the list to complete each definition.

distracted	concoction	sheriff	asthma	whiskey
occasion	extraordinary	semester	digestion	jewels

1. Something which is really special . . .   _____
2. A mixture or brew is a . . .   _____
3. A forgetful person seems to be . . .   _____
4. An officer of the law is a . . .   _____
5. A term at school is also called a . . .   _____
6. An example of an alcoholic beverage is . . .   _____
7. A disease of the respiratory system is . . .   _____
8. The Queen's crown contains many of these . . .   _____
9. One's birthday is a real . . .   _____
10. A mild diet will often aid one's . . .   _____

Questions:

1. What two people would the sick people of Green Lake go to see?

   _____

   _____

2. What did Sam suggest someone do if he or she wished to live to be 200-years-old?

   _____

   _____

 # HOLES

By Louis Sachar

3. What were four different things that Sam made from his onions?

   _____

   _____

4. Why wasn't Sam allowed to attend Katherine's classes?

   _____

   _____

5. Describe where Sam's onion field was located.

   _____

   _____

6. Why was Katherine disappointed when Sam finished fixing up the schoolhouse?

   _____

   _____

7. Why do you think Hattie Parker was so upset seeing Sam and Katherine kissing?

   _____

   _____

8. What deal did the sheriff offer Miss Katherine? What was her response? What does this tell you about her character?

   _____

   _____

9. Describe the fate of these characters.
   a) Sam:_____
   b) Mary Lou: _____
   c) Miss Katherine: _____
   d) Green Lake:_____

10. How did Miss Katherine get her revenge? Whom did she become?

    _____

    _____

Language Activities:

Pretend you are a newspaper editor for the Green Lake Daily News back in the 1800s and you are writing an editorial describing the events surrounding the death of Sam, the onion man (Chapter 26). Write the editorial, not only describing the events that happened, but also stating your opinion about what transpired and the way you feel about it.

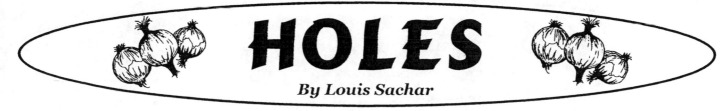

HOLES

By Louis Sachar

Chapters 27 and 28

Before you read the chapters:

Research some important facts about the lizard. What types are poisonous?

_____

_____

What other creatures are poisonous? _____

Vocabulary:

Choose a word from the list that means the same or nearly the same as the underlined word.

sparingly	obvious	patience	desperate	vile	vast	rummaging	declared

1. The warden of Camp Green Lake was a very **evil** person.   _____
2. Zero's need for a drink of water was **urgent**.   _____
3. The desert by the camp was very **large**.   _____
4. Stanley had a **tolerance** for spiders.   _____
5. The warden went **searching** through her locker for a weapon. _____
6. Water must be used **sparsely** in the desert.   _____
7. Stanley **asserted** his innocence to the judge.   _____
8. Stanley's nervousness among the campers was very **apparent**. _____

Questions:

1. Why did Stanley believe that Mr. Pendanski knew Mr. Sir was pouring Stanley's water onto the ground?

   _____

   _____

2. What upset the boys about Stanley and Zero's arrangement?

   _____

   _____

3. What kind of student did Stanley find Zero to be?

   _____

   _____

HOLES
By Louis Sachar

4. Explain why you think Stanley poured out the full canteen of water that Mr. Sir gave him? Defend your reasoning.

_____

_____

5. What was Zero's real name? Why do you think he got a nickname like zero?

_____

_____

6. Give this chapter a good title.

_____

_____

7. How did Kate know she was crazy?

_____

_____

8. Why did Kate say she was "so sorry" to Linda Miller?

_____

_____

9. Why do you think Kate wished she had been dead for the last 20 years?

_____

_____

Language Activities:

Put the following words from Chapters 27 and 28 in alphabetical order.

1. camera   _____

2. canteen   _____

3. chewed   _____

4. couldn't   _____

5. cabinets   _____

6. cabin   _____

7. can't   _____

8. could   _____

9. children   _____

10. peach   _____

 # HOLES

By Louis Sachar

Chapters 29 and 30

Before you read the chapters:

When does time seem to pass really slowly? Give an example from your own experiences.

_____

_____

When does time seem to pass very quickly?

_____

_____

Vocabulary:

Choose a word from the list to complete each sentence:

humid	delirious	horizon	counselors	holstered
character	concentrated	unconscious	investigation	obvious

1. Something which is very plain is to be _____.

2. Canned juice is usually _____.

3. A detective uses his or her power of _____.

4. A summer camp employs _____.

5. The gunfighter _____ his weapon.

6. The ballplayer was knocked _____ by the ball.

7. The little girl was _____ with joy on Christmas morning.

8. The sun appeared on the _____.

9. A day which is hot and damp is _____.

10. A person's personality is a part of his or her _____.

Questions:

1. Describe how the weather changed for the worse in Chapter 29.

_____

_____

HOLES

By Louis Sachar

2. Why couldn't anyone normally see the mountains after sunup?

_____

_____

3. To Stanley, where did it look like the lightning was coming from? Why might this be important?

_____

_____

4. When did Stanley learn not to doubt Zero?

_____

_____

5. Why did Stanley continue to let Zero dig his hole?

_____

_____

6. How did Mr. Pendanski think Stanley could teach Zigzag a lesson?

_____

_____

7. What did the Warden mean by her question to Ziggy, "Didn't you get a puppy for your birthday?"

_____

_____

8. Why did the Warden figure Zero would have to return to the camp?

_____

_____

Language Activities:

You are crossing a 20 mile stretch of desert on foot in the middle of summer. This is a trek that would take at least seven hours under the best conditions. Make a list of the items you would take with you on this hike, keeping in mind the conditions you will face and the fact that you must carry everything yourself. Also mention the type of clothing you would wear.

_____ _____ _____

_____ _____ _____

HOLES

By Louis Sachar

Chapters 31 and 32

Before you read the chapters:

Anger. Urges. Impulses.

Describe a time when you were angry. What were the results of your anger?

_____

_____

What does "**impulsive**" mean? _____

How can being impulsive be a bad thing?

_____

Vocabulary:

Read each of the sentences below.

> They'd still have to come back here **eventually**.
> One of the counselors was sitting guard by the water **spigot**.
> He tried to **convince** himself it wasn't possible.
> He's a **ward** of the state.
> The company of the president asked the recruit for **references**.
> Twitch was always **fidgeting**.
> The truck was stuck **lopsided** in the ground.
> Mr. Sir **deftly** chewed the sunflower seeds.

Define in your own words what you think each word means, then find out what the word really means.

Word	Guess	Real Meaning
eventually		
spigot		
convince		
ward		
fidgeting		
lopsided		
references		
deftly		

HOLES

By Louis Sachar

Questions:

1. What did Stanley feel that he should do, but didn't?

   _____

   _____

2. What responsibility did Stanley have to assume in Zero's absence?

   _____

   _____

3. What deal did Stanley decide to offer the Warden?

   _____

   _____

4. What did Stanley hope that Zero found on his own?

   _____

   _____

5. Why did X-Ray call the new kid Twitch?

   _____

   _____

6. What does "hot-wire the engine" mean?

   _____

   _____

7. What image did Stanley try to force out of his mind?

   _____

   _____

8. Why did Stanley steal the truck? Why wouldn't it move at first? How did Stanley's trip to the truck come to an expected end?

   _____

   _____

Language Activities:

Create a missing person's poster advertising Zero's disappearance from Camp Green Lake. Make sure you include a description of Zero (or a picture) and the amount offered.

HOLES

By Louis Sachar

Chapters 33 and 34

Before you read the chapters:

What is a "**mirage**"? _____

Give three examples of what mirages might be seen on a desert.

_____   _____   _____

Why might it be very upsetting for someone to witness a mirage?

_____

Vocabulary:

occasionally	systematic	frustration	random
encounter	cautious	imaging	mirage
encourage	mysterious	realized	

Draw a line to match the correct definition with each word. Use a dictionary and the context of the word in the novel to help you.

1. occasionally   deliberate

2. systematic   meet

3. frustration   fantasy

4. random   once in a while

5. encounter   careful

6. mirage   eerie

7. realized   aggravation

8. cautious   applaud

9. encourage   determined

10. mysterious   aimless

HOLES

By Louis Sachar

Questions:

1. What did Stanley head for when he escaped from the camp?

_____
_____

2. What did Stanley have for lunch?

_____
_____

3. What was unusual about the pool of water that Stanley found?

_____
_____

4. Why do you think it was so difficult for Stanley to estimate distances in the desert?

_____
_____

5. Why did Stanley change directions?

_____
_____

6. What unusual object did Stanley find?

_____
_____

7. How does the author end Chapter 34 on a suspenseful note?

_____
_____

Language Activities:

Copy out any three sentences from these two chapters and underline the verbs.

_____
_____
_____
_____
_____
_____
_____

HOLES

By Louis Sachar

Chapters 35 and 36

Before you read the chapters:

What does "**perseverance**" mean? _____

Why might this be an important trait for a person to possess?

_____

_____

Give an example from your own life when you persevered.

_____

_____

Vocabulary:

Synonyms are words with similar meanings. Using the context of the sentences below, choose the best synonym for the underlined words in each sentence.

1. Because of the room's poor **ventilation**, Stanley found it to be very hot and stuffy.
   a) aeration b) turbulence c) design d) lightning

2. Digging the hole left Zero **parched** and tired.
   a) exhausted b) naked c) dry d) frustrated

3. Mr. Sir was **distracted** from his duty by the loud yelling coming from the boys' dorm.
   a) encouraged b) detracted c) involved d) attracted

4. Kate's foot **protruded** into the aisle between the row of desks in the classroom.
   a) tripped b) slipped c) dropped d) extended

5. It was difficult for the warden to **concentrate** during the riot.
   a) think b) fight c) order d) dance

6. Stanley was afraid he would find **bacteria** on the old cup.
   a) insect b) reptile c) germ d) mouse

7. The camp was situated on the edge of an **actual** desert.
   a) obvious b) pretend c) imagined d) old

 # HOLES

By Louis Sachar

Questions:

1. How did Zero resemble an old jack-o-lantern?

   _____

   _____

2. What had Zero found buried under the boat?

   _____

   _____

3. Why was Stanley afraid to drink the concoction?

   _____

   _____

4. How did Zero know that Barf Bag had let the rattlesnake bite him?

   _____

   _____

5. Where were the boys heading out to?

   _____

   _____

6. The sploosh had both a positive and negative effect on Zero. Explain each.

   _____

   _____

7. What worried Stanley more than the thought of dying?

   _____

   _____

8. What obstacle did they meet at the far side of the lake? How did they overcome this?

   _____

   _____

Language Activities:

A **metaphor** is a figure of speech comparing two things without using the words like or as. An example is found in Chapter 35: "... a fiery ball balancing on top of Big Thumb. God was twirling a basketball."

Create two metaphors of your own.

_____

_____

HOLES
By Louis Sachar

Chapters 37 and 38

Before you read the chapters:

Zero has a fairly difficult time learning how to read. One of the reasons is the fact that English can be a difficult and confusing language.

Think of five words that are spelled quite differently from the way they sound.

_____ _____ _____ _____ _____

Now think of five words that are spelled almost exactly like they sound.

_____ _____ _____ _____ _____

Vocabulary:

Complete each sentence below with the correct word from the Word Box. Use a dictionary, if necessary, to look up the meaning of any words which are unfamiliar.

increments	zigzagged	concentrate	wrench	occasional
frail	violence	forearms	absorbed	droplets

1. The warden really had to _____ when filling out the form for the police.

2. Stanley tried to _____ the shovel from Zero's hands.

3. Stanley dug the hole in gradual _____.

4. Zero was very _____ in the task of cleaning out the latrine.

5. The boys watched _____ of water form on the window.

6. The old lady was very _____ and in poor health.

7. Many prison guards experience _____ as a part of their jobs.

8. The guard ate more than an _____ sunflower seed.

9. Stanley's _____ began to ache as he continued to dig.

10. The old beggar ran a _____ course across the football field.

HOLES
By Louis Sachar

Questions:

1. "Now that they really were almost there, it scared him." Why would this be frightening to Stanley?

   _____

   _____

2. What was one benefit the boys realized from Zero throwing up?

   _____

   _____

3. The boys knew they must be near water because of the presence of two things. What were they?

   _____

   _____

4. Why do you think Stanley realized he would never be able to climb the Thumb?

   _____

   _____

5. Why did falling into a muddy ditch turn out to be a good thing?

   _____

   _____

6. How did Stanley come to discover the onion?

   _____

   _____

Language Activities:

Find **three** examples of the following parts of speech from these two chapters.

Nouns	Verbs	Adjectives	Adverbs

HOLES

By Louis Sachar

Chapters 39 and 40

Before you read the chapters:

Some of the characters in this novel have the same name as famous writers. Research the titles of at least one book or poem that each of these men wrote.

Alfred, Lord Tennyson _____

Nathaniel Hawthorne _____

Arthur Miller _____

Vocabulary:

Analogies are equations in which the first pair of words has the same relationship as the second pair of words. For example **stop** is to **go** as **fast** is to **slow**. Both pairs of words are opposites. Choose the best word from the Word Box to complete each of the analogies below.

precipice	extend	comprehend	confession
leech	appreciate	deserted	indentation

1. Jump is to leap as cliff is to _____ .

2. Bold is to shy as misunderstand is to _____ .

3. Cherish is to _____ as strong is to hearty.

4. Love is to adore as abandoned is to _____ .

5. Unrepentance is to _____ as bad is to good.

6. Impression is to _____ as carpet is to rug.

7. Wrong is to right as contract is to _____ .

8. Bloodsucker is to _____ as kill is to slay.

HOLES

By Louis Sachar

Questions:

1. Why do you think Stanley went to the trouble of touching the giant precipice and saying "Tag, you're it"?

   _____

   _____

2. What was the problem with the drinking water they discovered?

   _____

   _____

3. What did Zero confess to Stanley?

   _____

   _____

4. How did the following people recommend little Rebecca Tennyson be treated for her illness?

   Sam: _____

   Dr. Hawthorn: _____

5. On what did Mrs. Tennyson blame her daughter's illness?

   _____

   _____

6. What do you learn about Sam's character from his conversation with Mrs. Tennyson?

   _____

   _____

7. Why didn't Stanley leave Zero to get the shovel while Zero was asleep? What does this tell you about Stanley's character?

   _____

   _____

Language Activities:

Beside each word from these chapters, write its root word.

digging	_____	softly	_____
actually	_____	normally	_____
violently	_____	snickered	_____
crawled	_____	contritely	_____
impossible	_____	buried	_____

 # HOLES

By Louis Sachar

Chapters 41 and 42

Before you read the chapters:

Define "**self respect**".

_____

Why is it important for a person to have self respect?

_____

What might be the consequences if a person does not have self respect?

_____

_____

Vocabulary:

Draw a line from each word on the left to its meaning on the right. Then use at least six of the numbered words in a short original paragraph that relates to _Holes_.

1.	contaminate	especially
2.	eventually	fate
3.	particularly	defile
4.	delirious	unhappy
5.	coincidence	dependant
6.	fugitive	accident
7.	destiny	outlaw
8.	miserable	personality
9.	ward	deranged
10.	identity	finally

Questions:

1. Why do you think it is easier to dig a hole in a dry spot than in one that is wet?

_____

_____

2. What is a "ward of the state"?

_____

_____

HOLES

By Louis Sachar

3. What do you think Zero meant when he first said he didn't have a mother, and then later said his mother was once a Girl Scout?

    _____

    _____

4. Was Zero right in saying that if he had kept Clyde Livingston's sneakers, neither he nor Stanley would have gotten sent to the camp? Explain your reasoning.

    _____

    _____

5. Stanley knew that they couldn't live on onions forever. Because of this, what did he know he and Zero must eventually do?

    _____

    _____

6. What made Stanley too happy to fall asleep in Chapter 42? Do you think it is important to feel this way about yourself? Explain you answer.

    _____

    _____

7. What does Stanley mean "It had to be destiny." (Page 185)? Do you believe in destiny for your own life?

    _____

    _____

Language Activities:

Chapter 42 ends with Stanley asking Zero the question, "You want to dig one more hole?"

Ending a chapter with this kind of sentence is called a **cliffhanger**. How else might Stanley have asked Zero about going back to look for the buried treasure, in a cliffhanger sort of way?

_____

_____

_____

_____

_____

_____

HOLES
By Louis Sachar

Chapters 43 and 44

Before you read the chapters:

In the space below, sketch a map showing how one would go from your home to your school.

Vocabulary:

Choose a word from the list to compete the sentence.

evicted	inexplicable	abruptly	indistinct	adjacent
exposed	precarious	portion	cluster	texture

1. The angry landlord _____ him from the apartment for not paying his rent.
2. Stanley could tell by the _____ of the burlap that it was very rough.
3. The voice on the phone was so _____ that Stanley could hardly hear it.
4. The success of the poor hockey team was completely _____.
5. The two friends had their lockers _____ to the gym door.
6. The newspaper reporter _____ the corrupt gangster.
7. the mountain climber was left in a _____ position on the cliff.
8. Stanley was brought _____ back to reality when he awoke at Camp Green Lake.
9. The waitress brought him a larger _____ of cake than his brother.
10. A _____ of trees marked the oasis.

Questions:

1. Zero had memories of when he was young enough to be in a crib. Describe your earliest memory.

_____

_____

 # HOLES

By Louis Sachar

2. Why do you think neither Stanley nor Zero wanted to be the first to take a drink?

_____

_____

3. Who is Jaffy? What was unusual about him?

_____

_____

4. Where did Zero stay for a month after his mother left him?

_____

_____

5. What do you think happen to Zero's father?

_____

_____

6. What was Stanley's reasoning in making the hole wider instead of deeper?

_____

_____

7. Why was Stanley so careful in digging out the object?

_____

_____

8. Why do you suppose the Warden waited until the boys finished digging the hole before she appeared.

_____

_____

Language Activities:

Interview at least three other students for their views of this novel. (Try to get both positive and negative comments.) Write a brief report putting these views together.

_____

_____

_____

_____

_____

_____

_____

_____

HOLES

By Louis Sachar

Chapters 45 and 46

Before you read the chapters:

What does it mean to **hallucinate**?

_____

When might a person hallucinate?

_____

What might a person hallucinate about?

_____

Vocabulary:

In each of the following sets of words, underline the one word which does not belong. Then write a sentence explaining why it does not fit.

1. unearth	suppress	restrain	conceal

_____

2. commotion	ado	peace	racket

_____

3. brighten	obscure	lit	illuminated

_____

4. frantic	calm	agitated	anxious

_____

5. culminate	initiate	start	begin

_____

6. delirious	excited	calm	agitated

HOLES
By Louis Sachar

Questions:

1. How do you think the Warden and the others discovered the boys were digging the hole?

   _____

   _____

2. What was Stanley's strategy in avoiding being bitten by the lizard?

   _____

   _____

3. What would be the result of a yellow-spotted lizard bite?

   _____

   _____

4. Why do you think the author starts the chapter with, "five hundred seconds later", instead of saying, "eight minutes and twenty seconds later"?

   _____

   _____

5. Why did Stanley have difficulty concentrating on the conversation going on around him?

   _____

   _____

6. Where did Stanley want to be when he died?

   _____

   _____

7. Why do you think Stanley found standing still to be even more strenuous than walking?

   _____

   _____

Language Activities:

Create and design a brochure promoting Camp Green Lake. Be sure to include some of the "imagined" benefits of this interesting facility that might attract more campers. You might wish to include activities which would take place in their "Wreck Room", pool, tennis courts, etc. Use your imagination!

HOLES

By Louis Sachar

Chapters 47 and 48

Before you read the chapters:

Why isn't it a good idea for a writer to include too many coincidences in a story?

_____

_____

Stanley and Zero are in a desperate situation as Chapter 47 opens. Predict what you think will happen to them. Give details.

_____

_____

Vocabulary:

Use a dictionary to find the meanings of the following words:

cyberspace: _____

justification: _____

tarantula: _____

pursuant:_____

hallucinations:_____

comprehend: _____

attorney:_____

authorization: _____

authenticated: _____

delirium: _____

Questions:

1. How did the boys discover that the lizards were, in fact, hungry?

_____

_____

 # HOLES

By Louis Sachar

2. What did Zero ask Stanley that was so amazing?

   _____

   _____

3. What excuse did the Warden offer for not releasing Stanley to the authorities?

   _____

   _____

4. What was there about the suitcase the left the Warden speechless?

   _____

   _____

5. How do you think Ms. Morengo "gave the appearance of being tall"? How would you describe her personality?

   _____

   _____

6. How did the Warden change her story about the suitcase?

   _____

   _____

7. Why did Stanley hesitate before leaving with his lawyer?

   _____

   _____

8. What was Zero's fate at the end of the chapter? How did this come about?

   _____

   _____

Language Activities:

Conflict is an important element in a novel. There are generally three types of conflict: person against person; person against self; and person against nature. For each of these types, find an example in the novel *Holes*.

   _____

   _____

   _____

   _____

   _____

   _____

   _____

Chapters 49 and 50

Before you read the chapters:

Predict what was in the suitcase that Stanley uncovered.

_____

_____

Vocabulary:

Write a sentence using the following words. Make sure that the meaning of each word is clear in your sentence.

investigating: _____

_____

recycle: _____

_____

eliminates: _____

_____

desperate: _____

_____

tedious: _____

_____

caviar: _____

_____

weathered: _____

_____

ingredients: _____

_____

 # HOLES

By Louis Sachar

Questions:

1. Why didn't the lizards bite Stanley and Zero?

   _____

   _____

2. What memory caused Stanley to feel shame?

   _____

   _____

3. Why did Ms. Morengo wish that the boys could bathe in Stanley's father's new invention?

   _____

   _____

4. What do you think it meant when it rained over Green Lake for the first time in 100 years?

   _____

   _____

5. Explain why the contents of the suitcase proved to be a disappointment at first.

   _____

   _____

6. How had Stanley's ordeals proved to be good for him?

   _____

   _____

7. How is there a double meaning to the phrase, "You will have to fill in the holes yourself"?

   _____

   _____

8. What did they call Stanley's father's invention? On what broadcast did Stanley see it advertised? Who was its spokesperson?

   _____

   _____

Language Activities:

Create a time line for *Holes* indicating the 10 most important events of the novel and the order in which they happened.

Answer Key

Chapters 1 and 2: *(page 9)*
Vocabulary: **1.** forbidden **2.** hover **3.** hammock **4.** warden **5.** shriveled

Questions:
1. Hot, arid - lizards, snakes, insects **2. a) & b)** very sick, perhaps die; **c)** probably die **3.** The lake dried up.
4. Keep your distance. **5.** Jail or Camp Green Lake. **b)** Camp sound like fun. **6.** Stanley's family was poor.

Chapters 3 and 4: *(page 11)*
Vocabulary: **1.** advisor **2.** proportion **3.** barrier **4.** condemned **5.** vagabond **6.** heirs **7.** huge
8. abandoned **9.** canvas **10.** to begin with **11.** security

Questions:
1. His destination was in the middle of nowhere. **2.** Mrs. Bell referred to Stanley as the heaviest kid in the class.
3. A way to recycle old sneakers. **4.** Kate only kissed the men she killed. **5.** Suspenseful. How bad did it look?
6. Barren and desolate. A few run-down buildings and some tents. The only plant life were two tall trees.
7. A long-sleeved orange jumpsuit, an orange T-shirt, and yellow socks. **8.** They were to report it to one of the
counselors. **9.** Because the Camp was in the middle of a desert, there was no where to run.

Chapters 5 and 6: *(page 13)*
Vocabulary: **1.** shadow **2.** early **3.** leaflet **4.** broccoli **5.** contorted **6.** coax **7.** gather

Questions:
1. Mr. Pendanski – younger than Mr. Sir, not as scary looking. Top of head shaved. Had a thick, curly beard.
His nose was badly sunburned.
2. a) Squid **b)** Rex **c)** Lewis **d)** Magnet **e)** Armpit **f)** Zigzag **g)** Mom **h)** Zero
3. There's nothing inside his head. **4.** Answers may vary. **5.** Sweet Feet. **6.** He'd led the American League
in stolen bases the last three years and he was the only player to ever hit four triples in one game.
7. No one believed they fell from the sky. **8.** His mother thought that because he was innocent all that was
necessary was for him to tell the truth and he would be exonerated. Answers may vary. **9.** Answers may vary.

Language Activities: pen – dance – key

Chapters 7 and 8: *(page 16)*
Vocabulary: **1.** a **2.** c **3.** d **4.** b **5.** a **6.** b **7.** b
Questions:
1. To build character. **2.** The ground was hardest at the surface. **3.** A heart full of love.
4. Myra's head is as empty as a flowerpot. Carry a piglet to the top of mountain every day and let it drink from the stream.
5. He and his descendants would be doomed for all eternity. **6.** He used his cap to protect his hands.
7. Zero was very quiet and would spit in the hole each day when he finished.
8. He probably felt guilty because he didn't carry Madame Zeroni up the mountain as he promised.
9. He spat in the hole. **10.** Yellow-spotted lizards. **11.** Tie in to topic of lizards.

Language Activities: people, lullabies, chunks, cacti, canteens, women, thumbs

Chapters 9 and 10: *(page 19)*
Vocabulary: sprawled: to sit or lie with limbs spread out; *vinyl:* shiny plastic; *intensity:* passionate,
conviction; *commercial:* business, advertisement; *miracle:* wonder, marvel; *awesome:* amazing
fossilized: turned to bone; *blistered:* rubbed raw

Questions:
1. Nearly everything in the room was broken. **2.** You're hurting before you even get started. **3.** So not to worry
his mother. **4.** Caveman. Stanley was large and quiet. **5.** Every muscle and joint in his body ached **6.** It meant
that there once was water where now was a desert. **7.** He proved he could find something in his digging.

Chapters 11 and 12: *(page 21)*
Vocabulary: **1.** smug **2.** responsible **3.** obvious **4.** veterinarian **5.** senseless **6.** accomplish **7.** expand
8. society **9.** appropriate **10.** expression

Questions: **1.** He had poor vision. **2.** He was the smallest **3.** He was confident and good at bullying **4.** He felt accepted. **5.** He fantasized about Derrick being beaten up by his new friends from Camp Green Lake. **6.** Answers may vary. **7.** His no-good-dirty-rotten-pig-stealing-great-great-grandfather. **8.** Answers may vary. **9.** Zero is worthless

Chapters 13 and 14: *(page 23)*
Vocabulary: **1.** chose **2.** occasionally **3.** glisten **4.** turquoise **5.** authority **6.** produce **7.** sifted **8.** design **9.** engraved **10.** nervous

Questions: **1.** The cloud stayed visible but didn't offer any shade or rain. **2.** A gold tube about as long as a finger with KB engraved on it. **3.** They turn it in early the next day. **4.** Stanley moved up a place in the line. **5.** Answers may vary. **6.** Mr. Pendanski had just filled the canteens.

Chapters 15 and 16: *(page 25)*
Vocabulary: Answers may vary.

Questions: **1.** To make sure they didn't miss anything. **2.** They had found the object in his hole, not X-Ray's. **3.** Hidden cameras. **4.** So he would remember to come back and see what else he could find. **5.** X-Ray had very poor vision. **6.** She was proud of his character. **7.** He was very poor with no television.

Chapters 17 and 18: *(page 27)*
Vocabulary:

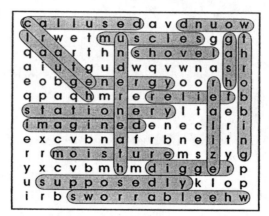

Questions: **1.** Zigzag accidently hit him on the side of the head with a shovel while digging. **2.** By the fourth day all of the holes met. **3.** Warden was frustrated and used Armpit as an example. **4.** So the boys wouldn't make fun of him. **5.** He had no respect for Zero. **6.** Read and write. **7.** His heart.

Language Activities: **1.** Mr. Pendanski was a guard at Camp Green Lake. **2.** Stanley's friends included Armpit, Zero and Magnet. **3.** Clyde Livingston played for the Chicago Cubs. **4.** My favorite book is called Lost in Space.

Chapters 19 and 20: (page 29)
Vocabulary: Part 1 – **1.** invigoration **2.** product **3.** healthful **4.** honored **5.** advance
Part 2 – **1.** condemned **2.** recede **3.** agony **4.** toxic **5.** ingredient

Questions: **1.** The boys were white, black and Hispanic, but out on the lake they were all reddish brown. **2.** Answers may vary. He was embarrassed and defensive in the morning. **3.** The bag was tossed to him and when he missed it, it broke open in his hole. **4.** Answers may vary. Magnet stole the sunflowers. Answers may vary. **5.** Stanley's answers didn't add up. **6.** The nail polish was toxic. **7.** The Warden scratched Mr. Sir. Answers may vary – probably to maintain her authority.

Chapters 21 and 22: *(page 31)*
Vocabulary: **1.** abandoned **2.** demented **3.** haven **4.** grow **5.** comfort **6.** modify **7.** quote **8.** surprise **9.** small letters **10.** wound **11.** invigorate

Questions: **1.** Stanley was afraid Mr. Sir would take his humiliation out on him. **2.** Seventeen days – God's Thumb. **3.** The rattle lets you get out of its way. **4.** Zero. His hole was smaller than the others. Answers may vary. **5.** He multiplied 26 by 2 in his head and got the correct answer. **6.** He would dig part of Stanley's hole each day. Having Zero dig his holes left Stanley with more energy to teach Zero how to read. **7.** In his mother's bathroom. A lipstick container. Kate Barlow.

Language Activities: **1.** rattlesnake **2.** bathroom **3.** lipstick **4.** grandfather **5.** everybody **6.** lowercase **7.** outside **8.** sunflower **9.** wasteland **10.** everyone

Chapters 23 and 24: *(page 33)*
Vocabulary: Answers may vary.

Questions: **1.** Cinnamon, cloves, nutmeg and other spices. **2.** Food for the angels. **3.** Teacher. **4.** His feet smelled like dead fish. **5.** Bully – loud and stupid. Answers may vary. **6.** Mr. Sir choked the boy. **7.** Not to go too fast or too slow. **8.** Poured his water onto the ground.

Language Activities: peach jam, cobbler, fruit drink, pie

Chapters 25 and 26: *(page 35)*
Vocabulary: **1.** extraordinary **2.** concoction **3.** distracted **4.** sheriff **5.** semester **6.** whisky **7.** asthma **8.** jewels **9.** occasion **10.** digestion

Questions: **1.** Dr. Hawthorn and Sam, the onion man. **2.** Eat nothing but raw onions. **3.** Ointments, lotions, syrups, and pastes. **4.** He was a Negro. **5.** On the other side of the lake. **6.** She missed his company. **7.** Answers may vary. **8.** If Kate kissed him he wouldn't hang Sam. Kate tried to slap him. Kate was honorable and would not compromise her principles. **9.** Sam – shot and killed; Mary Lou – shot and killed; Miss Katherine – shot the sherrif and became an outlaw; Green Lake – dried up. **10.** She shot the sheriff and became Kissing Kate Barlow.

Chapters 27 and 28: *(page 37)*
Vocabulary: **1.** vile **2.** desperate **3.** vast **4.** patience **5.** rummaging **6.** sparingly **7.** declared **8.** obvious

Questions: **1.** He gave Stanley extra water. **2.** They felt Stanley was getting out of work. **3.** Quick. Diligent. **4.** Answers may vary. **5.** Hector Zeroni. Last name sounds like Zero. **6.** Answers may vary. **7.** Answers may vary – talked to herself, lived alone, did bizarre things. **8.** Linda was stuck with Trout. **9.** She missed Sam.

Language Activities: **1.** cabin **2.** cabinets **3.** camera **4.** can't **5.** canteen **6.** chewed **7.** children **8.** could **9.** couldn't **10.** peach

Chapters 29 and 30: *(page 39)*
Vocabulary: **1.** obvious **2.** concentrated **3.** investigation **4.** counselors **5.** holstered **6.** unconscious **7.** delirious **8.** horizon **9.** humid **10.** character

Questions: **1.** The weather became unbearably humid. **2.** Because of the haze. **3.** Coming out of the thumb-shaped rock formation. This might help to explain his great-grandfather's statement, "I found refuge on God's thumb." The lightning was coming out of the thumb as if it were the thumb of God. **4.** When it came to math. **5.** It was better than digging. **6.** By hitting back and teaching the bully a lesson. **7.** Sarcasm. **8.** No water – extreme heat would force him back.

Chapters 31 and 32: *(page 41)*
Vocabulary: Answers may vary.

Questions: **1.** He felt he should go after Zero. **2.** Dig Zero's hole. **3.** He would tell the Warden where they found the tube if she wouldn't scratch Zero. **4.** God's Thumb. **5.** He was always fidgeting. **6.** Start the car without a key. **7.** Zero's fate out on the desert. **8.** To go after Zero. At first he didn't have it in gear. He drove it into a hole.

Chapters 33 and 34: *(page 43)*
Vocabulary: **1.** once in a while **2.** deliberate **3.** aggravation **4.** aimless **5.** meet **6.** fantasy **7.** determined **8.** careful **9.** applaud **10.** eerie

Questions: **1.** The direction of Big Thumb. **2.** One sunflower seed. **3.** It was a mirage. **4.** No landmarks; hazy; extreme heat. **5.** He saw something closer than Big Thumb and headed toward it. **6.** The remains of an upside down boat. **7.** By having an orange sleeve reach out from under the boat.

Chapters 35 and 36: *(page 45)*
Vocabulary: **1.** a) **2.** c) **3.** b) **4.** d) **5.** a) **6.** c) **7.** a)

Questions: **1.** Face orange from dirt, features sunken from thirst and exhaustion. **2.** Sixteen jars of sploosh (preserved peaches). **3.** It might make him sick. **4.** He'd taken off his shoe. **5.** The Big Thumb. **6.** Gave him strength; made him sick. **7.** His parents not knowing what happened to him. **8.** Cliff. They scaled it.

Chapters 37 and 38: *(page 47)*

Vocabulary: 1. concentrate 2. wrench 3. increments 4. absorbed 5. droplets 6. frail 7. violence 8. occasional 9. forearms 10. zigzagged

Questions: 1. He was afraid there would be no water. 2. The gnats stayed with Zero's vomit. 3. Weeds and bugs. 4. It was too steep and he was too weak. 5. They found a way to get water. 6. Digging for water.

Chapters 39 and 40: *(page 49)*

Vocabulary: 1. precipice 2. comprehend 3. appreciate 4. deserted 5. confession 6. indentation 7. extend 8. leech

Questions: 1. Answers may vary. 2. The water was dirty. 3. Zero stole Clyde Livingston's sneakers. 4. Sam – onion tonic; Dr. Hawthorn – leeches on her stomach. 5. Eating bad meat. 6. Answers may vary – proud, humble, considerate to his old donkey. 7. He didn't want Zero to think he'd been deserted.

Language Activities: dig; actual; violent; crawl; possible; soft; normal; snicker; contrite; bury

Chapters 41 and 42: *(page 51)*

Vocabulary: 1. defile 2. finally 3. especially 4. deranged 5. accident 6. outlaw 7. fate 8. unhappy 9. dependant 10. personality

Questions: 1. Dirt is heavier when wet and clings to the shovel. 2. An orphan. 3. His mother left when he was very young. 4. Answers may vary. 5. Return to civilization across the desert. 6. He liked himself. Answers may vary. 7. Answers may vary.

Chapters 43 and 44: *(page 53)*

Vocabulary: 1. evicted 2. texture 3. indistinct 4. inexplicable 5. adjacent 6. exposed 7. precarious 8. abruptly 9. portion 10. cluster

Questions: 1. Answers may vary. 2. Answers may vary – pride. 3. Zero's stuffed giraffe. 4. The playscape at Laney Park. 5. Answers may vary. 6. The treasure was probably not buried too deeply. 7. So he wouldn't ruin it. 8. To make sure they were at the right hole – Answers may vary.

Chapters 45 and 46: *(page 55)*

Vocabulary: 1. unearth 2. peach 3. obscure 4. calm 5. culminate 6. calm

Questions: 1. Answers may vary. 2. Keep absolutely still. 3. Death. 4. Seems even longer. 5. Exhaustion. 6. In the snow with his mother. 7. Time passed more slowly.

Chapters 47 and 48: *(page 57)*

Vocabulary: Answers may vary.

Questions: 1. One ate a scorpion. 2. He realized that Stanley's last name was "Stanley" spelled backward. 3. They didn't have the proper authorization. 4. The suitcase had Stanley's name on it. 5. She was very confident and projected this. 6. Stanley put the Warden's things inside the suitcase. 7. He didn't want to leave Zero. 8. He was released because there was no record of him at the camp.

Chapters 49 and 50: *(page 59)*

Vocabulary: Answers may vary.

Questions: 1. The lizards didn't like the smell of onions or someone who had eaten a lot of them. 2. Fishing his notebook out of the toilet. 3. His father invented a product that eliminates foot odor. 4. Answers may vary. 5. Jewels were of a poor quality and worth only $20 000. 6. Lost weight, built character. 7. Filling in the real holes that had been dug; and filling in between the lines as to what happened to Zero and Stanley. 8. Sploosh. The Super Bowl. Clyde Livingston.